THE

U·F·O HUNTER'S

HANDBOOK

THE

U·F·O

HUNTER'S

HANDBOOK

by Caroline Tiger

PENGUIN BOOKS

PENGUIN BOOKS

Published by the Penguin Group

Penguin Books Ltd, 27 Wrights Lane,
London W8 5TZ, England

Penguin Putnam Inc., 375 Hudson Street,
New York, New York 10014, USA

Penguin Books Australia Ltd, Ringwood,
Victoria, Australia

Penguin Books Canada Ltd, 10 Alcorn Avenue,
Toronto, Ontario, Canada M4V 3B2

Penguin Books India (P) Ltd, 11 Community
Centre, Panchsheel Park, New Delhi -
110 017, India

Penguin Books (NZ) Ltd, Cnr Rosedale
and Airborne Roads, Albany, Auckland,
New Zealand

Penguin Books (South Africa) (Pty) Ltd,
5 Watkins Street, Denver Ext 4,
Johannesburg 2094, South Africa

On the World Wide Web at: www.penguin.com

Penguin Books Ltd, Registered Offices:
Harmondsworth, Middlesex, England

First published 2001
1

Designed and Illustrated by Paul Kepple
and Timothy Crawford @ Headcase Design,
Philadelphia, Pennsylvania

Made and printed in England by Clays Ltd,
St Ives plc

British Library Cataloguing in Publication Data
A CIP catalogue record for this book is
available from the British Library

ISBN 0-141-31417-6

PHOTOGRAPHY CREDITS

Pg. ii: Joe Felzman/FPG

Pg. vi: Vladimir Pcholkin/FPG

Pg. 7: (bottom right) JF-MJC/FPG

Pg. 10: Bettmann/CORBIS

Pgs. 12–13: Bettmann/CORBIS

Pg. 15: Art Montes de Oca/FPG

Pgs. 16–17: Art Montes de Oca/FPG

Pg. 19: Chris Michaels/FPG

Pg. 22: Art Montes de Oca/FPG

Pg. 28: (earth photo only) VCG/FPG

Pg. 36: Stuart Dike/FPG, (circle photo inset)
Hulton-Deutsch Collection/CORBIS

Pg. 41: CORBIS

Pg. 42: Bettmann/CORBIS

Pg. 47: (top left) Art Montes de Oca/FPG,
(top right, middle left) CORBIS, (middle right,
bottom left) Bettmann/CORBIS, (bottom right)
Charlie Franklin/FPG

Pg. 54: Chip Simons/FPG

Pgs. 70–71: Joe Felzman/FPG

Pg. 74: (UFO over city only) Navaswan/FPG

Pg. 81: Bettmann/CORBIS

CONTENTS

1. OFTEN SAUCER-SHAPED   2. USUALLY SPOTTED FLYING IN THE SKY
3. OFTEN SPOTTED IN RURAL AND DESOLATE AREAS
4. ACCOMPANIED BY LIGHT BEAMS OR RAYS OF LIGHT

WHAT ARE UFOS?

Chances are you're already a UFO Hunter. Have you ever seen an object in the afternoon or night sky that kind of looked like an aeroplane, but was moving too slowly to be one? How about a twinkly light that resembled a star except that it was darting through the sky? How about aliens – ever noticed that a friend seemed a little too weird to be from this planet? Maybe you've even felt like *you* were from a different planet sometimes!

The moment you questioned what these flying objects were – or whether friends were aliens – you became a UFO Hunter. 'UFO' stands for 'Unidentified Flying Object'. To say you've seen a UFO is to say you've seen something and don't know what it is. And to say you're a UFO Hunter is to say you believe there might be life on other planets and that maybe, just maybe, they've come here to check out what's happening on *our* planet.

Experts in ufology (the study of UFOs) say that 90 per cent of reported unidentified flying objects are later identified as satellites, weather balloons, stars, meteors, fireballs or other known objects, making them really IFOs (Identified Flying Objects). But the other 10 per cent just can't be explained away by any experts. Your best bet for working out whether the object you saw is a star or an alien craft is to know exactly what to look for.

UFOs come in many shapes and sizes and can appear at any time of the day or night, so you need a checklist like the one in this book to classify the object you've seen. *The UFO Hunter's Handbook* will tell you where and when you're most likely to see a UFO, and then how to record and report a sighting accurately so you can find out for sure if it's one of the unexplained 10 per cent.

But all good detectives need background information before they go into the field, so let's take a moment to review some UFO basics.

UFO ABCS

UFOs have not always been called UFOs. In 1947, when pilot Kenneth Arnold was flying over the Cascade Mountains in Washington State, USA, searching for a crashed military aircraft, he saw some crescent-shaped objects flying towards the sun. His description of the objects 'flying like saucers skipping across water' led to the term 'flying saucers'. In the 1950s, the U.S. Air Force came up with the more all-inclusive 'Unidentified Flying Objects', perhaps because they knew by then that such sightings aren't limited to saucer-shaped objects. In fact, UFOs come in many forms.

There are two major types of UFO. The first and most commonly reported type is the 'nocturnal light'. Nocturnal lights come in all shapes and sizes. Some are small spots of light; some are larger and look like balls. They often move in strange and unpredictable patterns.

The other type of UFO you're most likely to see is a 'craft'. They are usually shaped like saucers, boomerangs, diamonds, cigars or triangles. They tend to have bright lights – often glowing red or white. At other times they are multicoloured. Sometimes they are reported to emit beams or shafts of light. They can be seen during the day or at night. Some UFOs move at incredible speeds, while others hover or move slowly through the sky.

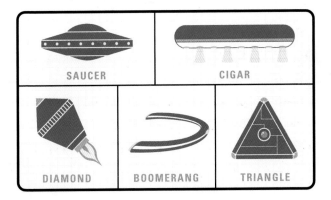

SAUCER

CIGAR

DIAMOND

BOOMERANG

TRIANGLE

UFOS DON'T FLY BY THEMSELVES

If your hunt is successful, you will see an object worthy of reporting. If it's even more successful, the alien craft just may abduct you, or perhaps you'll meet some of the aliens who are operating the UFO.

Ufologists have come up with three classifications of such encounters. A **Close Encounter of the First Kind** (CE1) is when a UFO appears within five hundred feet or less of you.

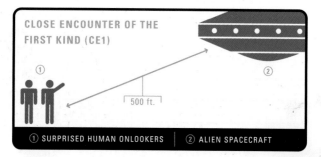

CLOSE ENCOUNTER OF THE FIRST KIND (CE1)

① 500 ft. ②

① SURPRISED HUMAN ONLOOKERS ② ALIEN SPACECRAFT

CASE STUDY: CE1

TIME: 3.45 P.M., July 28, 1976

PLACE: Winsted, Connecticut, USA

Thirteen teenage boys and their camp leader are hiking through the Connecticut woods. They've just stopped for water and a snack when they hear a high-pitched whine coming from the sky. When the campers look up through a clearing in the trees, they see a metallic, flat-bottomed saucer about twenty feet wide. It is surrounded by a purple glow and topped by a dome glowing red. The UFO hovers in place for about twenty seconds before rising higher into the sky and then vanishing so fast, you could've blinked and missed it.

In a **Close Encounter of the Second Kind** (CE2), the UFO will physically do something to you or perhaps to the environment. If the grass nearby is burned or the trees damaged, the UFO has left what ufologists call 'landing traces', and you've just had a CE2.

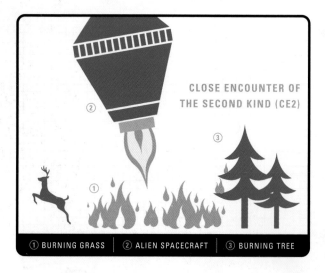

CLOSE ENCOUNTER OF
THE SECOND KIND (CE2)

① BURNING GRASS | ② ALIEN SPACECRAFT | ③ BURNING TREE

CASE STUDY: CE2

TIME. 5.00 P.M., January 8, 1981

PLACE: Trans-en-Provence, France

Elderly Renato Niccolai is kneeling in his garden when he hears a whistling sound behind him. He looks over his shoulder to see an object moving through the sky. When it lands in a nearby alfalfa field, he runs up a hill to get a better look at the grey object. He later describes it as 'two saucers upside down, one on top of the other'. Soon after, the UFO rises up and shoots off in the same direction from which it came. Niccolai finds it hard to convince his wife – or anyone else for that matter – that he's telling the truth.

But everyone believes him after several investigators take soil samples of the field and find evidence, or 'landing traces', that it has been exposed to radiation of some kind.

If you experience a **Close Encounter of the Third Kind** (CE3), you'll see an alien or may even be abducted by it.

CLOSE ENCOUNTER OF
THE THIRD KIND (CE3)

① FRIGHTENED HUMANS | ② ALIEN SPACECRAFT | ③ ABDUCTEE

CASE STUDY: CE3

TIME: Late at night, September 19, 1961

PLACE: Portsmouth, New Hampshire, USA

Barney and Betty Hill are driving down a road in New Hampshire when they notice a UFO following their car. What Barney later describes as a 'mind voice' instructs him to drive off the road and into some deep woods. There the Hills come upon what appear to be six men standing on the road, illuminated by an orange glow. The men approach the car and guide Barney and Betty into a spaceship. The couple later recall in dreams and under hypnosis that the extraterrestrials took them into the

UFO, performed some tests on them to determine how humans are different from their own species, and then delivered the Hills back to their car. The aliens acted cold and businesslike, as if they were scientists using the Hills as their specimens. Betty is reported as saying that only the 'head' alien showed any signs of kindness or compassion.

The Hill Abduction became one of the most famous abduction stories in UFO history, because Barney and Betty Hill were among the first people to be abducted by a UFO – and to recall their experience and report it.

ABDUCTIONS

The **abduction phenomenon** has been growing since the Hills' experience in 1961. For some reason, abductions seemed to increase considerably during the 1980s and have been going strong ever since. The Hills' report is typical of most abductions: earthlings are taken on board an alien spacecraft and examined by aliens who are cold, clinical and businesslike in demeanour. Sometimes, the aliens will even give an abductee a mission to complete once back on earth, such as relaying a message about the decaying environment or the survival of the human species.

Respected Harvard University psychiatry professor John E. Mack has paid special attention to the abduction phenomenon. In his 1994 book titled *Abduction: Human Encounters with Aliens,* he printed interviews with various contactees and abductees and tried to identify a common thread that explained the aliens' intent. Mack suggested

CAREFUL! DON'T GET TOO CLOSE TO A CLOSE ENCOUNTER OF THE SEC

in his book that these aliens come here to expand our own consciousness, that they know more than we do, and that they have important information to pass on. He established the Program for Extraordinary Experience Research (PEER) to explore such paranormal encounters.

No one can say what the pilots of an unidentifiable craft will decide to do when you encounter them, but hopefully this book will help to prepare you for whatever situation may arise, even if you're deemed special enough by visiting aliens to have a Close Encounter of the Third Kind. Since all close encounters start with a more distant encounter (we hope), the first order of business is the sighting of the aliens' craft.

IMAGINE

John Lennon, a member of the rock band the Beatles, saw a UFO one night in August 1974, from the balcony of his New York City apartment. He described it as having a flattened dome with a bright red light on top and a circle of white lights on the underside. It flew directly above him without making any sound. The musician did not even hear the hum of an engine.

Lennon was fascinated by UFOs and was known to read *Flying Saucer Review*, a magazine about UFOs. He even included them in the lyrics to a song on his *Milk and Honey* album: 'There's UFOs over New York, and I ain't too surprised'.

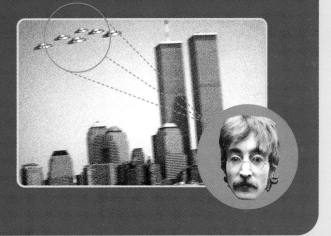

HAVE YOU EVER BEEN ABDUCTED?

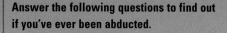

Answer the following questions to find out if you've ever been abducted.

1. Have you ever experienced 'missing' or 'lost' time?

2. Have you ever had a dream in which you were paralysed in bed while another being watched you or examined you?

3. Do you have any unusual scars or marks with no possible explanation for how you received them?

4. Have you ever had X-ray vision, even just for a few minutes?

5. Have you ever seen balls, flashes or beams of light?

6. Have you ever woken up to find yourself in a location other than the one where you went to sleep?

7. Have your friends noticed anything different about you lately?

Y N   8. Have you ever heard voices that seem to come from nowhere?

Y N   9. When you see pictures of aliens, do you feel sick to your stomach?

Y N   10. Do you have recurring memories or dreams of flying through the air?

Y N   11. Do you have dreams in which you pass through a solid object, like a wall or closed window?

Y N   12. Do you have strong phobias and an eerie feeling of being watched?

Y N   13. Do you feel like you 'have a mission' to complete?

Y N   14. Are you often tormented by images of needles or other medical tools, like stethoscopes or tongue depressors?

Y N   15. Do you think you are psychic?

If you answered 'yes' to at least three of the above questions, you may have been abducted.

SNACKS

WATCH

CAMERA

NOTEBOOK

BINOCULARS

TORCH

THE UFO AND ALIEN FIELD GUIDE

You're alone in a park in the middle of a city. Dusk is falling and there's a chill in the air. Your friends have headed home, but for some reason your instinct is to stay put. In a few minutes, your patience is rewarded.

From where you stand, you see an arc of light out of the corner of your left eye. When you turn your head to look, there it is: a slow-moving disc decorated with flashing purple lights. A UFO! You watch as it hovers over your head for a moment and then darts away into the darkening sky.

What's wrong with this scenario? Well, it depends on who you ask. From many people's perspectives, seeing a UFO at all is a stroke of luck and a singular experience. But from a UFO Hunter's point of view, it can be much more than that.

If the person in the above scenario had the proper equipment, it would have increased his or her chances of later working out what it was. A UFO? A meteor? A weather balloon? Something else? And data must be recorded during a sighting if you plan to report it to the proper authorities.

The question is this: do you want to be a person who's *seen* a UFO, or do you want to be a UFO *Hunter*?

If you answered 'UFO Hunter', read on for the whats, hows, wheres and whens of a successful hunt.

WHAT YOU NEED

- Torch
- Watch (to record times of activity)
- Binoculars equipped for night viewing
- Video or still camera and tripod
- Small coins and a ruler to hold at arm's length to gauge the sizes of objects seen against them
- Thermometer to record air temperature at regular intervals
- *The UFO Hunter's Handbook* checklist (see pages 52–3) and notebook (see pages 88–9).
- Tape recorder to record observations
- Witnesses (It's more believable when more than one hunter agrees on a sighting.)

- Pen or pencil

- Snacks (You may be waiting a while.)

- A drink (to wash down those snacks!)

HOW

1. Get some of your friends together. There's safety in numbers, and the more witnesses, the more likely it is that others will believe you.

2. Wear a good pair of trainers. You never know when you'll need to run. Fast.

3. Be patient. You may not find anything on your first few times out searching.

4. Know where you're going and how long you *should* be gone, so that people back at home can know when to start looking for you to make sure you're okay.

5. And don't forget those snacks.

WHERE

Okay, you've got your notebook, your pen and some pals. But where should you go to stake out these suckers? It's a big, wide world out there and chances are a UFO is not going to end up in your back garden.

Here's the good news: to an alien, our world is not so big. After all, these beings are approaching by aircraft. Have you ever been in an aeroplane, where you're so high up that people look like fleas and cars look like ants? Have you seen the pictures of Earth taken by NASA spacecraft? Whole continents are the size of a dinner plate!

From an alien's point of view, our planet is not at all overwhelming. Besides, they're going to keep coming back until they've seen everything – like those people who travel across the United States in camper vans, or across Europe with backpacks. So really, you don't have

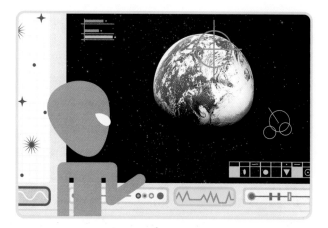

to go far from your house. You just have to be in the right place at the right time.

Still, there are certain tricks of the trade that will up your chances.

1 Get out of a city or built-up area. Evidence shows that UFOs are often sighted in rural areas, maybe because the sky is easier to see without big buildings in the way

or the lights of a city obscuring the lights of a UFO. Also, there's a lot more open space for UFOs to land.

2 Go to higher ground – a hilltop or plateau where you are closer to the sky and have a better vantage point.

3 Choose a night with a clear sky and good weather.

WHEN

Night watches are the most successful. According to Chicago's Center for UFO Studies (CUFOS), one of the world's premier ufology groups, most sightings occur around 9.00 P.M., with a second peak of activity around 3.00 A.M.

To increase your chances of seeing a UFO, it's best to go to an area known for repeated UFO activity. UFO activity tends to strike in the same areas again and again. When frequent activity occurs in one place, it's called a 'flap' or a 'wave'. The areas known for waves of sightings are called 'hot spots'. In the United States, there have been UFO sightings in every state, but the greatest number have been in the Northeast and the Southwest.

THE TEN HOTTEST STATES IN AMERICA

ARIZONA. Just outside Phoenix, as recently as 1997, there was a sighting of many glowing orbs of light in the sky. In June of that year, *USA Today* reported that the citizens of Phoenix saw a huge craftlike object hovering behind all of the glowing orbs. Even Arizona's governor demanded an investigation, of which there've been a few, but no answers . . . yet.

CALIFORNIA. At Giant Rock in the Mojave Desert stands the Integratron. No, it's not a new video game or a follow-up to the Macarena—it's a thirty-eight-foot-high dome, built in 1947 by a former aircraft engineer named George Van Tassel. Van Tassel claimed the structure could somehow rejuvenate live human cell tissue and that he built it with the help of extraterrestrial (ET) visitors.

FLORIDA. Gulf Breeze, between Pensacola and Santa Rosa Island, has been known as one of the hottest spots in the USA since 1987, when a local businessman took the first of a series of pictures of a strange craft lined with windows. The same businessman was later abducted and claimed to have had an 'implant' placed in his brain. To this day, groups of skywatchers meet at Gulf Breeze almost every night.

GEORGIA. La Grange, a small town about sixty miles southwest of Atlanta, sits on the edge of the Troup-Heard Corridor, which has been known for its UFO activity for the

TOP TEN UFO HOT SPOTS IN THE UNITED STATES

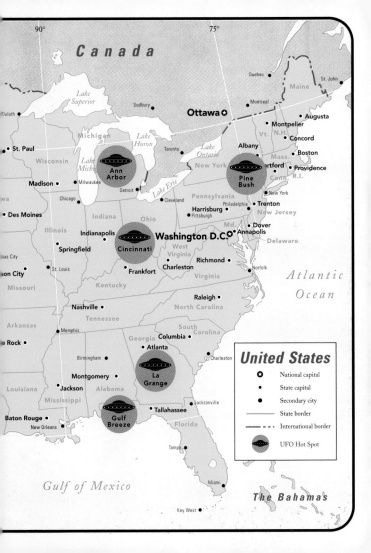

last fifty years. Reports include sightings of fireballs, giant saucers and tubelike objects.

MICHIGAN. There was a wave of sightings in Ann Arbor in 1966, and since then there haven't been too many, but it's still considered worth a shot by many in the USA.

NEVADA. The town called Rachel is home to an Air Force base called Area 51, more famously the place where, in 1989, a physicist named Bob Lazar claimed to have helped a crashed flying saucer escape. The main road leading to Rachel has been renamed 'The Extraterrestrial Highway'.

NEW YORK. Pine Bush, a tiny town about eighty miles north of New York City, is a mecca for UFO Hunters. There have been many sightings there since 1969. One Pine Bush citizen, a musician named Ellen Crystal, has taken nearly two thousand pictures of UFOs she's seen there.

OHIO. Nearly all of Ohio is a potential location for a sighting, but experts particularly recommend sites near Cincinnati. And if you like baseball, you're in luck, because Cinergy Field – home of the Cincinnati Reds – is a hotbed of activity.

UTAH. Crop circles, those mysterious formations that appear overnight, imprinted in fields of wheat or other crops, first appeared in Cache County in 1996. Witnesses to one of the circles said they could hear a high-pitched sound when they sat in the middle of them.

WASHINGTON. This West Coast state was the setting for Kenneth Arnold's 1947 sighting. (He was the pilot who coined the term 'flying saucer'.) There have also been many UFO sightings in the town of Yakima, especially from 1972 to 1974, often witnessed by fire wardens keeping watch for forest fires from tall towers.

THE TEN HOTTEST PLACES ON THE PLANET

AFRICA. Many sightings have been made from the summit of Pico de Teide on Tenerife, one of the Canary Islands off the northwest coast of Africa.

AUSTRALIA. Queensland, on the northeastern tip of the continent, is where the Great Barrier Reef meets the rainforest. It's also home to crop circles—the unexplained,

CROP CIRCLES POSSIBLY CREATED BY ALIENS

precisely swirled circles laid down in crop fields and thought to be caused by aliens. The first circle on record showed up in Queensland in 1966.

BELGIUM. A wave of UFO sightings happened here beginning in November 1989 and continuing for two years. Almost all of the sightings were of huge, triangular crafts with bright flashing lights.

BRAZIL. São José, a Brazilian city 300 hundred miles northwest of the larger city of São Paulo, is a hot spot for UFO Hunters. For centuries this area had been haunted by strange lights known locally as the 'mother of gold'. São José has one of the highest rates of alien abductions in the world.

ENGLAND. Among many hot spots here are the Pennines on the Lancashire–Yorkshire border, where there's an extensive history of sightings of strange lights. Long ago the hills were associated with witchcraft or demons. In fact, women suspected of witchery were rolled down the hills in barrels. If they survived, they were considered guilty and put to death. If they died during the witchery test, they were innocent.

FRANCE. Because of the number of sightings in the southeast region of France known as Provence, this country is second only to England in the European standings for most UFO activity. The example of a CE2 that you read in Chapter 1 happened in Provence, as did one peculiar sighting by a man and his son who for months afterwards had identical red triangular marks on their stomachs, right over their belly buttons.

ITALY. In 1985, a young couple in northeast Italy reported a sighting of two creatures who were more than six feet tall, flat as pancakes and wearing silver suits. And in 1987, three men were driving along a mountainous road in Italy when a UFO appeared over their car.

MALAYSIA. This peninsula south of Thailand is home to peculiar sightings of tiny alien creatures. In August 1970, in the region called Penang, there were a number of sightings of three-inch-tall beings, complete with mini UFOs. They reportedly wore one-piece suits and had very large ears.

NORWAY. Responding to reports of sightings from many different small communities in the region of the Hessdalen Valley, a team of ufologists set up camp there for five weeks in 1984. In fifty-six days, they reported having 188 sightings!

UNITED STATES. In addition to the smokin' hot states already listed, there's Texas, home of the infamous Texas Triangle. This is an area that is largely desert and canyons (and no people). One side of the triangle is about 180 miles long. The kinds of sightings here have included everything from UFOs stopping cars on the main road to reports of blue-green blobs and V-formations of lights.

THE HOTTEST SPOT IN THE UNIVERSE (THAT WE KNOW OF)

CYDONIA, MARS. Cydonia is the locale for 'the Face on Mars', a raised area on the terrain of that planet whose features resemble a face with two eyes, a nose and a mouth. The Face on Mars first showed up in images taken by NASA's Viking orbiter. While NASA dismisses this as a trick of the light, it's believed by others to be proof of life on Mars.

Richard Hoagland, a former NASA consultant, even claims to have seen other pictures showing the remains of a city in Cydonia. He reports that the city and the face are aligned in a way that may have pointed to the place where the sun rose on the Martian solstice half a million years ago. (How did he work *that* out?)

MARS

'THE FACE ON MARS'

① ② ALIEN SPACECRAFT

③ ④ ⑤ ⑥ HUMAN OBSERVERS

①

②

③

④

⑤

⑥

WHAT TO DO IF YOU SEE A UFO

When you see a UFO, you should collect a lot of information so that you can make a complete report of your sighting.

If you take careful enough notes, you may later realize that the UFO you saw was actually a weather balloon or a shooting star. Then it becomes an IFO, or an Identified Flying Object. Unfortunately, this will mean that your object was not paranormal, but the information could still help you the next time you go out searching.

Here are some important things to remember when you go on a skywatch.

1) Keep track of the time the observation begins and note the time of any changes in the UFO's direction. Be careful using a digital watch, though, because sometimes if you're too close to a UFO, electronics can stop working. (UFOs have also been known to drain all the power out of moving cars.)

2) Make an immediate sketch of what you saw and write down as many details as you can. Record the date, time and exact location of the sighting. Get witnesses and carefully take down their names and addresses in case the investigator asks. (But don't discuss the details of the

sighting with them until after you have recorded your own account – this could lead to confusion.)

(3) If you hold a ruler up at arm's length and measure the size of the object, and someone else further away does the same thing, the combined information, along with the lengths of your arms, can help to determine how large the object really was.

(4) A camera is a good tool for documenting your sighting, but beware: the media may suspect that your photographs have been faked. To avoid this problem, make sure the pictures have identifiable things in them, like a recognizable building or the tree line, because a photo of just the sky with an object *could* have easily been faked. And again, the more pictures by different people, the more believable your story.

(5) Above all, stay calm and pay attention to the details.

Did the craft hover or did it zoom around the sky? In which direction did it go? Take notes and try to remember the experience as well as you can. All your accumulated information will be crucial when it is time to report the sighting.

And remember, a lot of people think it's funny to pull a hoax (and it can be), so you have to be careful to weed out the real sightings from those being faked by others.

The most common UFO hoax is a prank balloon, which involves tying a flare or candle to a helium-filled balloon. Once launched, the light will make the balloon look like a glowing orb in the night sky.

It's important to be informed and a little suspicious, so you can do your detective work. Knowing this is half the battle.

IS IT REAL, OR IS IT A HOAX? YOU DECIDE

Real Hoax

Real Hoax

Real Hoax

Real Hoax

Real Hoax

Real Hoax

ALBERT BENDER

CLAIM TO UFOLOGY FAME: pursued by the real-life men in black

CREDENTIALS: founded the *Flying Saucer Bureau* based in Bridgeport, Connecticut, USA

ACTIVE IN UFOLOGY: since 1952

THE DETAILS: He quit the Flying Saucer Bureau soon after he founded it, claiming he was warned off by mysterious 'men in black'. People began to disbelieve Bender's claims only when his descriptions of the men in black started to vary every time he retold the story of his encounter. They went from something akin to secret agents (as they were portrayed in the blockbuster film in 1997) to shape-changing aliens.

BUDD HOPKINS

CLAIM TO UFOLOGY FAME: an advocate for people who believe they were once abducted by aliens

CREDENTIALS: wrote two books detailing his work with abductees and travels worldwide lecturing about his theories; founded the *Intruders Foundation*, a support group for abductees

ACeTIVE IN UFOLOGY: 1970s to present

THE DETAILS: Hopkins discovered that many abductees experience 'missing time', or periods of time they can't account for. He proposed that these periods of missing time mask terrifying real-life experiences, and he teamed up with psychiatrists to start a systematic data-gathering campaign.

LINDA MOULTON HOWE

CLAIM TO UFOLOGY FAME: the first researcher to connect cattle mutilations with UFO activity

CREDENTIALS: award-winning TV documentary filmmaker; among other organizations, the Mutual UFO Network (MUFON) presented Howe with an award honouring her investigation of unusual phenomena

ACTIVE IN UFOLOGY: 1990s to present

THE DETAILS: Howe made the documentary *A Strange Harvest* (1993), which looked at the worldwide phenomenon of mysterious animal mutilations that have been occurring since the 1950s. In her documentary and in her book *An Alien Harvest*, Howe convincingly linked the mutilations to alien visitations.

DR. ALLEN J. HYNEK

__CLAIM TO UFOLOGY FAME:__ his first book was the basis for Steven Spielberg's film *Close Encounters of the Third Kind* (1977)

__CREDENTIALS:__ scientist and founder of the *Center for UFO Studies* (CUFOS)

__ACTIVE IN UFOLOGY:__ 1948 to his death in 1986

__THE DETAILS:__ Hynek became interested in UFOs as a young astronomer in Ohio, where he worked as the science consultant to the U.S. Air Force from 1948 to 1969. He founded CUFOS in 1973 and travelled around the world for the last decade of his life to tell as many people as possible that UFO studies have a basis in science.

PROFESSOR JOHN E. MACK

__CLAIM TO UFOLOGY FAME:__ the most prominent university professor to openly support the existence of UFOs

__CREDENTIALS:__ Harvard Medical School psychiatrist and Pulitzer Prize–winning author

__ACTIVE IN UFOLOGY:__ 1991 to present

his theories

THE DETAILS: Mack risked his reputation with his colleagues to champion the claims of abductees. He proposes that they're part of an alien plan to transform our society.

DR. JACQUES VALLEE

CLAIM TO UFOLOGY FAME: the model for a key character in *Close Encounters of the Third Kind*

CREDENTIALS: computer expert, scientist and award-winning science-fiction author

ACTIVE IN UFOLOGY: 1960s to present

THE DETAILS: Vallee, a scientist, left his native France in the 1960s to come to California and help Allen Hynek found CUFOS. Since then he (along with his wife, Janine) has conducted many investigations from his home in San Francisco and introduced many new theories to the field of ufology.

CHECKLIST

Here is a list of the important questions you need to ask yourself when you see a UFO. The list is a quick reference for the time of the actual sighting, but it's also a good idea to read through the questions before you even start your skywatch. That way, when it does happen, you can focus all of your attention on the alien craft.

○ What time is it?

○ How warm or cold is it outside?

○ What's the date?

○ Where are you?

○ Write down the specifics – sketch a map with landmarks like trees, roads and houses.

○ Does the UFO have lights of any kind?

○ Just one or multiple?

○ Are they constant?

○ Pulsating?

○ Flashing?

○ How is it shaped?

○ Like a boomerang?

○ Like a cigar?

○ Like a disc?

○ If not any of the above, then how?

- How fast does it move?

- Does it speed through the sky?

- Does it hover in one spot and dart away?

- Or is it in between?

- In which direction does it move?

- Vertically?

- Sideways?

- In circles?

- If there is more than one UFO, are they in any kind of formation, like a 'V'?

- Can you see any beings on board?

- What do they look like?

- Are they small or large?

- How many eyes do they have?

- Are they flesh-coloured?

- Sketch one in your notebook.

- What are they doing?

- Are they staring back at you?

- Did they exit the craft at any time?

- What effects, if any, did the sighting have on you?

- Anything physical?

- Did anything happen to the surroundings – the trees and the grass?

UP CLOSE
AND
PERSONAL

Descriptions of aliens differ from abductee to abductee and from contactee (someone who's made contact with an alien) to contactee, but there are some qualities that seem to reappear in reports from all different people.

This could be because they're all seeing the same aliens, or aliens from the same planet. Or it could be that they made up the whole thing and weren't creative enough to come up with their own alien. (As we mentioned earlier, hoaxes are, unfortunately, a common occurrence in the world of UFO hunting. This includes fabricated sightings of aliens.)

Some sceptics suggest that people who make up stories of UFO sightings take the aliens' physical makeup straight from pop culture sources, like TV and films. But film and TV aliens aren't all alike. Look at E.T. He's about three feet tall, with crinkly, hairless skin and a flat face. That's very different from the sinister, octopus-like aliens who terrorized the world in *Independence Day*.

And then there's Mork – the alien played by actor Robin Williams in the 1970s sitcom *Mork and Mindy* – who was very hairy, but certainly not as short as Alf, and he didn't have claws. And in the classic Steven Spielberg film *Close*

Encounters of the Third Kind, the aliens look more like E.T. than Alf, but not at all like Mork. For even more variety, think *Star Wars* and *Star Trek*.

Here are the general categories and features of the different types of alien people have described from their real-life close encounters:

THE GREYS

There are several subcategories of Greys, though all are greyish in colour.

GREY TYPE A

Physical features: They're about 4.5 feet tall with large heads and black wraparound eyes (kind of like a fly's). Besides their large eyes, they have limited facial features – just a slit for a mouth and no nose.

Hail from: a star system neighbouring Orion.

Psychological makeup: Beware of Grey Type A – they are emotionless and cold. They function in a rigidly defined social structure that holds science and conquering other worlds as main priorities. They come to Earth primarily to collect specimens (that's you) for their scientific studies.

Spotted in: Nevada and New Mexico.

GREY TYPE B

Physical features: seven to eight feet tall with facial features similar to those of Grey Type A, except Bs have big noses. (The better to smell you with!)

Hail from: Orion.

Psychological makeup: Less aggressive than Type A, but still considered hostile. Bs tend to gain influence through negotiations with those in power, so if you're not powerful, they're probably not coming after you.

Spotted in: Eastern Russia and the Aleutian Islands (off Alaska, in the Bering Sea).

GREY TYPE C

Physical features: These are the shortest of the Greys — sometimes Grey Cs are as short as 3.5 feet tall. They have facial features similar to those of As, which means almost none at all.

Psychological makeup: There's less known about Cs, because they visit earth less often than As or Bs. But we do know they're hostile, so beware!

Hail from: A star system near the shoulder of Orion called Bellatrax.

Spotted in: Hardly ever spotted.

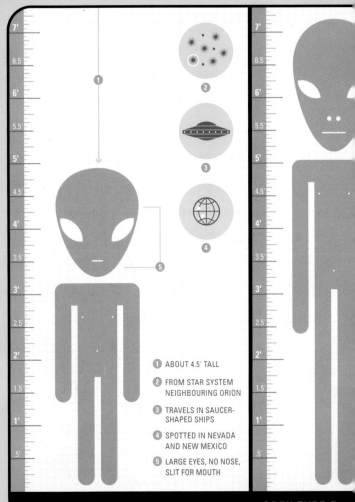

1. ABOUT 4.5' TALL
2. FROM STAR SYSTEM NEIGHBOURING ORION
3. TRAVELS IN SAUCER-SHAPED SHIPS
4. SPOTTED IN NEVADA AND NEW MEXICO
5. LARGE EYES, NO NOSE, SLIT FOR MOUTH

GREY TYPE A: EMOTIONLESS AND COLD

GREY TYPE B: HO

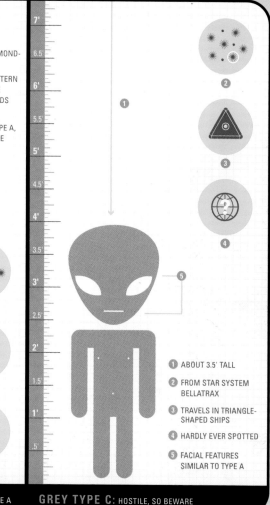

1. ABOUT 7' TALL
2. FROM ORION
3. TRAVELS IN DIAMOND-SHAPED SHIPS
4. SPOTTED IN EASTERN RUSSIA AND THE ALEUTIAN ISLANDS
5. SIMILAR FACIAL FEATURES TO TYPE A, EXCEPT BIG NOSE

1. ABOUT 3.5' TALL
2. FROM STAR SYSTEM BELLATRAX
3. TRAVELS IN TRIANGLE-SHAPED SHIPS
4. HARDLY EVER SPOTTED
5. FACIAL FEATURES SIMILAR TO TYPE A

GGRESSIVE THAN TYPE A   **GREY TYPE C:** HOSTILE, SO BEWARE

HUMANOIDS

There have been many types of Humanoid sightings. Some ufologists think Humanoids are actually the offspring of the Greys and the humans they abduct. These creatures could be your brothers and sisters!

Physical features: Distinctly human. They stand on two legs, have arms, a head and a face with eyes, a nose and a mouth. At the same time, there's something disturbingly 'off' about these familiar features. Their heads are bulging, their faces are long and their foreheads are wide. Or their eyes are lidless slits, or in some cases are so large they take up half their face. In most Humanoid sightings, the alien is fair-skinned with blond hair.

Psychological makeup: More evolved than the Greys or Reptilians, the Humanoids seem to feel some sort of kinship with humans and are likely to be kind.

Hail from: Arcturus, Vega, Pleiades, Orion or Sirius.

Spotted in: All the major hot spots.

THE REPTILIANS

Some researchers believe the Greys are merely preparing the way for a full-scale invasion of Reptilian aliens.

Physical features: Reptilian!

Psychological makeup: These beings are not friendly. Repeat: not friendly. They're said to view humans as humans would view a herd of cows – in other words, they wouldn't mind eating you medium-rare, or tipping your neighbour over while she's asleep.

Hail from: A small planet that's becoming more and more unable to adequately support their ever-growing population – so they just may be moving to Earth soon.

Spotted in: Florida and South America.

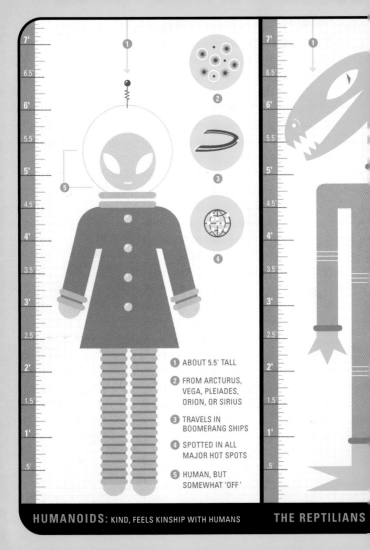

1 ABOUT 5.5' TALL

2 FROM ARCTURUS,
VEGA, PLEIADES,
ORION, OR SIRIUS

3 TRAVELS IN
BOOMERANG SHIPS

4 SPOTTED IN ALL
MAJOR HOT SPOTS

5 HUMAN, BUT
SOMEWHAT 'OFF'

HUMANOIDS: KIND, FEELS KINSHIP WITH HUMANS

THE REPTILIANS

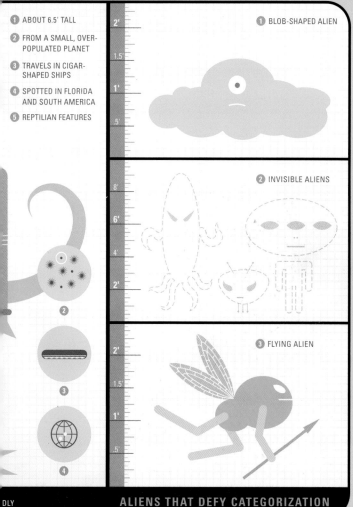

1 ABOUT 6.5' TALL

2 FROM A SMALL, OVER-POPULATED PLANET

3 TRAVELS IN CIGAR-SHAPED SHIPS

4 SPOTTED IN FLORIDA AND SOUTH AMERICA

5 REPTILIAN FEATURES

1 BLOB-SHAPED ALIEN

2 INVISIBLE ALIENS

3 FLYING ALIEN

ALIENS THAT DEFY CATEGORIZATION

ALIENS THAT DEFY CATEGORIZATION

Some variations on the above include flying aliens (with actual wings), aliens in silver spacesuits and aliens with some type of headgear, like a helmet or antennae. People who are lucky enough to come upon unsuspecting aliens might find them behaving like scientists, gathering samples of soil or plants. They may be holding objects such as jars or tubes, perhaps to collect the samples.

They could be blob-shaped, like Teletubbies, or they could be amorphous – able to change shape in an instant. They could be invisible or so tiny that there's no way for the human eye to detect their movements. An alien could also be a gargantuan creature, more like the monsters in horror films than lovable E.T.

ARE YOU – OR IS SOMEONE YOU KNOW – AN ALIEN?

- Is your skin particularly scaly in spots?

- Do you dream in a strange language that doesn't sound like anything spoken on Earth?

- Do you sometimes feel as though no one really understands you?

- Do you ever crave a food that you can't seem to find in your own supermarket?

- Do you sometimes feel homesick even when you are at home?

HOW TO COMMUNICATE

According to contactees, most ETs communicate through mental telepathy. If that's the case, you won't have to worry about trying to talk back, because it will just happen. You'll hear a 'voice' and will somehow be able to communicate telepathically in return. It's been reported that aliens are born with this amazing ability. Humans, however, have to work much harder to develop telepathy skills.

Aliens have also been known to screech or chirp like birds. At other times, they've been described as speaking a strange, foreign language that is characterized by grunting.

If they do speak English, it may be difficult to understand their accent. In that case, you can try to use body language, but **let the alien make the first move.** After all, they may not know that a wave or a handshake is a friendly gesture. The last thing you want to do is cause some kind of misunderstanding that will make the alien suspicious of your intentions.

To communicate that you mean well, you should try to relax your face and body. Smile, and don't make any sudden movements. And if you find you're too shocked to possibly think of something to say, try one of the friendly starters listed here.

CONVERSATION STARTERS WITH FRIENDLY OVERTONES

- Nanoo. Nanoo.
- I'm okay. (Point to self.) You're okay. (Point to alien.)
- Any trouble finding the place?
- Take me to your leader.
- Can I offer you a snack? (Proceed to offer snacks.)

If your friendly overtones are met only with violence and anger on the alien's part, you have no choice but to defend yourself. Here are some suggestions for doing just that. Remember, though, the best choice in the presence of hostile aliens is to run as fast as you can away from them. If running won't help, here are some alternatives.

BEWARE! NOT ALL ALIENS ARE FRIENDLY, AS CAN BE SEEN IN THIS INVASI

HOW TO DEFEND YOURSELF

① Just say 'No!' You have to be forceful, but it often works.

Use phrases like 'Go away!', 'Leave me alone!', or 'Beat

it, ET – Go home!'

② Use physical resistance. Don't try to kill them (you don't

know what kind of strange weapons they may have

hidden), but make it clear that you don't want to go with them. Once they've got you on their craft you will be helpless to defend yourself or to get assistance.

③ If resisting physically doesn't seem to be working, try sending mental messages. Picture yourself shielded by a force field of white light. If an alien can read your mind, he may understand.

④ Start acting really strange – do cartwheels back and forth, or speak gibberish. If they think you're not a 'typical' human, they may decide not to take you on board their ship and do tests on you.

⑤ For some reason, aliens are afraid of cats. Maybe on other planets, cats are untamed and ferocious creatures. For whatever reason, it's always smart to have a cat nearby. They also have a sixth sense for detecting aliens.

HOW TO DEFEND YOURSELF

① JUST SAY 'NO!' | ② PHYSICAL RESISTANCE | ③ PSYCHIC SHIELD

④ CARTWHEEL DEFENCE | ⑤ FELINE SCARE TACTIC

REPORTING THE INCIDENT

If you believe you have seen a UFO, and you can agree on all the details of its motion, shape, colours, etc. with some-one else, it's very important that you report it. You never know – if at least two of you are sure you saw it, there could be others elsewhere who did as well. Only when everyone gets a report in can it be called an actual sighting.

Don't be surprised if, when you feel you're getting closer and closer to the truth, you get a visit from some men in black. That film with Will Smith, where he pummels the ugly aliens? It's based on a true story.

THE REAL MEN IN BLACK

In 1952, UFO Hunter Albert Bender founded the Flying Saucer Bureau in his home town of Bridgeport, Connecticut, USA. The organization researched UFOs and also published a magazine on the subject.

Soon after its founding, Albert Bender left the bureau. According to an article from *Astronet Review* (February 1992), he announced that, while part of the mystery of UFOs had been uncovered, it could not be made public. Soon after that announcement, he gave an interview to a local paper, saying that he'd been visited by 'three men in black', who warned him to stop his investigation.

Several other prominent UFO researchers also reported visits from similar men in black. And though no one knows who these men work for, we can gather these identifying details from their visitees:

- MIBs travel in twos or threes.
- They drive old black Cadillacs and dress in black suits.
- Their mission is to silence and intimidate witnesses.
- MIBs aren't overtly violent, but they will leave visitees with strange symptoms such as blurred vision or headaches.

Some have guessed that they're government agents. Whoever they are, they don't want anyone getting too close to the truth.

WHO YOU GONNA CALL?
NOT THE TABLOIDS!

Beware of tabloids who offer to buy your story. Poor-quality newspapers are often accused of stretching the truth. If your sighting is reported there, it may not be taken seriously elsewhere.

Bogus reporting from tabloids dates back to 1969, when the *National Bulletin* in the USA wrote that the astronauts of Apollo 11's mission to the Moon had seen UFOs after their historic July 16 landing. The *Bulletin* went so far as to fabricate a transcript of radio communications between the astronauts and Mission Control.

NOT THE GHOSTBUSTERS EITHER

Calling the police may not be the best option, unless someone's injured or property has been severely damaged, or if you think more people are in danger. The police may not take you seriously, no matter how convincing your evidence. It's best to call a UFO organization that is prepared to deal with all sorts of reports.

The British UFO Research Organization (BUFORA) collects and conducts research on UFO phenomena throughout the United Kingdom. They can be contacted on 01227 722 916 with your sighting details. Their address is as follows:

BM BUFORA

London WCIN 3XX

www.bufora.org.uk

You can also get in touch with the following organizations in the USA by post or via the Internet.

National UFO Reporting Center
P.O. Box 45623
Seattle, Washington, USA 98145
www.nwlink.com/~ufocntr

Mutual UFO Network, Inc. (MUFON)
103 Oldtowne Road
Seguin, Texas, USA 78155-4099
Fax: 210.372.9439
www.mufon.com

Remember that you are not alone. Such important, respected people as former US President Jimmy Carter and the astronomer who discovered Pluto are among those who have reported sightings of UFOs. And studies from psychologists working with contactees and UFO Hunters show that these people tend to be of above-average intelligence, are highly observant and have excellent visual creativity. Tell that to any sceptics who may cross your path!

The truth is out there – so keep your feet on the ground, your eyes on the skies and go for it!

REPORTS OF UFO SIGHTINGS REQUIRE EXPERT ANALYSIS

APPENDIX: FURTHER READING AND VIEWING

To find out more about UFOs and UFO Hunting, try some of the essential books and films listed below.

10 ESSENTIAL UFO BOOKS

Abduction: Human Encounters with Aliens by John E. Mack (nonfiction): Mack summarizes thirteen case studies of abductees. He says that aliens are real and that they abduct humans for two purposes: (1) to tell us how to prevent the destruction of the Earth's environment, and (2) to create children who are part human and part alien.

The Alien Encyclopedia by Andrew Donkin (nonfiction, ages 9 to 12): This detailed directory of TV and film space creatures enables the reader to identify most types of alien.

Aquila by Andrew Norriss (fiction, ages 9 to 12): Two boys come across a mysterious buried spaceship in a quarry and manage to get it working. However, they soon discover some unexpected problems.

Chariots of the Gods by Erich von Däniken (nonfiction): Von Däniken studied ancient history by visiting prehistoric ruins and lost cities. In this book, he concludes that Earth has been visited by aliens throughout history, all the way back to ancient times. And, von Däniken says, we are all part alien.

Childhood's End by Arthur C. Clarke (science fiction): Giant silver spaceships suddenly appear in the skies above every major city on earth. Manned by aliens, the ships rid the world of ignorance, disease, poverty . . . and humans.

Communion by Whitley Strieber (nonfiction): This is Whitley Strieber's story of what happened to him when he was abducted by aliens. It was on *The New York Times* bestseller list for twenty-five weeks – that means a lot of people bought this book!

Contact: A Novel by Carl Sagan (fiction): A multinational team of astronauts ventures deep into outer space, where they come face to face with an advanced alien civilization! (The 1998 movie starring Jodie Foster was based on this book.)

My Life Among the Aliens by Gail Gauthier (fiction, ages 9 to 12): Everything about Will's life is normal, except for one thing – there's something about his mother's baking that attracts hungry aliens from outer space!

My Teacher Is an Alien by Bruce Coville (fiction, ages 9 to 12): A trio of enterprising school pupils conduct an investigation to find out if their teacher is from another planet.

UFO Briefing Document: The Best Available Evidence by various authors (nonfiction): These are actual documents from secret government files. The authors of this book think that aliens and UFOs are real, and the government knows it. They say the government has been trying to hide the truth from you and everyone else!

ESSENTIAL UFO FILMS

The Abyss (1989). A civilian diving team is enlisted to search for a lost nuclear submarine and instead encounters an underwater alien species.

Alien (1979), and sequels through to *Alien: Resurrection* (1997). An intergalactic crew, led by the fearless female alien-fighter Ripley, does battle with a particularly vicious invader.

Close Encounters of the Third Kind (1977). After an encounter with UFOs, a scientist feels irresistibly drawn to an isolated area in the wilderness where something spectacular is about to happen.

Contact (1998). Jodie Foster stars as a woman who receives a message from a distant star, which, once decoded, tells her how to build an incredible transporter.

E.T. the Extra-terrestrial (1982). A hugely popular tear-jerker of a film about a very cute alien who finds himself stranded on Earth and who is looked after by a lovable family.

Fire in the Sky (1993). This film recreates the strange events that happened on November 5, 1975, in the town Snowflake, Arizona. Travis Walton works as a logger in the woods. While driving home from work, he and his colleagues encounter a UFO. Travis disappears, and for the next five days his colleagues are accused of murder. When he reappears, at first he doesn't remember that he had gone, but in time the terrible memories come back . . . true story!

Independence Day (1996). The aliens are coming, and their goal is to invade and destroy. Fighting superior technology, man's best weapons are Will Smith, Jeff Goldblum, Bill Pullman and, oh yeah – the will to survive.

Lost in Space (1998). In 2058, in hopes of opening a gateway to a new planet for denizens of an overcrowded Earth, the Robinson family is launched into space, accompanied by a he-man pilot and the weasely doctor who tried to sabotage the journey.

Mars Attacks! (1996). The Earth is invaded by Martians with irresistible weapons and a cruel sense of humour.

Men in Black (1997). Two men who keep an eye on aliens in New

York City must try to save the world after the aliens threaten to blow it up.

My Stepmother Is an Alien (1988). An alien is sent on a secret mission to Earth, where she appears as a gorgeous, attractive and single lady. Her special mission is to make contact with a rather nerdy young scientist, who's quite overwhelmed by her attentions and isn't aware of the connection between her arrival and his work.

Superman (1978). An alien orphan is sent from his dying planet to Earth, where he grows up to become his adoptive home's first and greatest superhero.

UFO HUNTER'S NOTEBOOK

SIGHTING DATE: thursday february 12th 2

SIGHTING TIME: 9:00 pm (around that time)

LOCATION: Woodglen somthing (a round our friends house) Calgary, Alberta, calgary

TEMPERATURE: +3°C

UFO DESCRIPTION:

LIGHTS: Red and green and white, Flash

SHAPE: circulur

SPEED: Very slow

DIRECTION: east   sideways

FORMATION (IF MORE THAN ONE):

only one.

ALIEN DESCRIPTION (IF ANY ARE SIGHTED):

TYPE:

SIZE:

NUMBER OF EYES:

COLOUR:

ACTIVITY OBSERVED:

no aleins seer

COMMENTS: There were about four people who saw it. We were in a car. it was very close. And "All the small things was playing (good memories!

alex, jaz, shaby, bred

UFO HUNTER IDENTIFICATION

"WE COME IN PEACE"

The bearer of this ID has read and understood *The UFO Hunter's Handbook*. By signing below, the bearer agrees to practice safe and responsible research for alternate life.

Any extraterrestrial reading this ID should return it immediately (with its owner) to the address printed below, care of planet Earth. DO NOT perform medical experiments on registered UFO Hunters. REMEMBER that all UFO Hunters require oxygen, water, and carbon-based food to survive. Thank you for your cooperation.